THE BA
GU
K
FIT

Written by Sam Kotadia

Psychologist Sam Kotadia professionally helps top flight footballers stay focused and conquer the Bad Loser that lurks within us all. With this series of playful guides, Sam chucks his expertise out the window and offers strategies that are sure to lead to failure at every turn.

Illustrated by Nick Hilditch

Illustrator Nick Hilditch went off golf as a child when his Dad made him caddy for him in exchange for pocket money. So, in a way, his Bad Loser got the better of him before he'd ever taken a swing. His sport of choice is piercing inflated egos with the pointiest of pointy pencils. He teamed up with Sam to bring his skewed vision and irreverence to the Bad Loser's highly questionable advice.

Enjoy the game!

TO

....

FROM

....

Get out of bed when your alarm goes off, ready to exercise

You were born fit, there is no need to take your new regime too seriously.

When your alarm goes off, put it on snooze for at least 2 hrs.

When you finally get
out of bed, you will be
full of energy and ready
to tackle your exercise
regime.

Avoid eating too much before exercise

A quick Whopper Meal at McDonalds is the food champions are made of.

Plenty of sugar and fat will set you up nicely for a gruelling work out.

Make sure that you order an extra vanilla milkshake for the hard work ahead.

3

Don't push too
hard on the treadmill.

It is important that you are fully committed when you exercise.

When you step onto the treadmill, push yourself to the limits!

Make sure that you select the fastest speed just to make it interesting.

No need for the Rocky soundtrack for extra motivation; you are a born athlete.

Make sure that you
drink plenty of water.

When you have reached your supreme level of fitness there is no need to be hydrated.

If anything water is extra baggage and will slow you down.

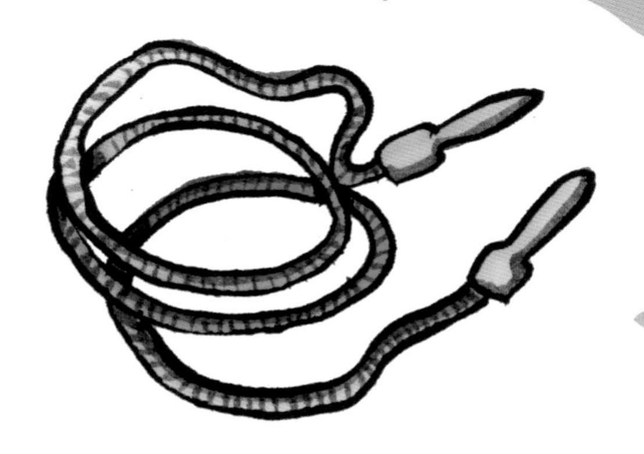

Drinking will also increase your chances of needing to go to the toilet.

What a waste of time!

Watch out for dog shit when you are running

When you are running along the streets you have a sixth sense for dog shit.

Experts like yourself can stealthily skip out of the way of such terrors.

If you happen to see a dog on your travels be sure to kick it out the way.

There is only room for one runner on these streets.

Try not to admire yourself
for too long in the mirror

When you look as good as you do, it is hard not to admire yourself in the mirror.

See those long stares in the mirror as a reward for all of your hard work.

Make sure that you admire yourself from all angles.

There is no need to do it privately; put on a show for those around you.

Don't try and lift too much weight

Somtimes less is more.

Not! This is what weaklings say when they are struggling.

Go hard and go big every time you work out.

Ensure that you are lifting at least your own body weight for each exercise.

No pain, no gain!

Stay out of the pub after exercise

There is no harm in the odd pint or five after a rewarding work-out.

Bask in front of your mates and make sure that they can see your physical prowess.

Only the tightest
of tops will do;
make sure that
everyone in
the pub feels
intimidated by
your amazing
body.

Focus on your own routine and don't be distracted by anyone else's

You cannot resist the temptation to compare and measure up to those around you.

There is no harm in flattering yourself by making comparisons.

Looking this good doesn't come easy!

Treat yourself by looking at those inferior to you whilst exercising. Feel sorry for them as they struggle to lift the weight you can do in your sleep!

Work all body parts equally

You know what your favourite body parts are.

Don't get bogged down by your weaker areas. Forget they even exist. Out of sight, out of mind is your motto.